THE HANGOVER SURVIVAL GUIDE

BY MARTIN BAXENDALE

CONTENTS

INTRODUCTION

Welcome to the definitive guide to hangover prevention and survival.

This book is the result of many, many years of dedicated and tireless personal research into the terrible after-effects of drinking far too much day after day after day.

Essential research carried out regardless of the dangers (countless work-related injuries involving staggering, bumping into things, falling off bar stools, and trying to snog strangers in the street) and the many health risks (including a liver that now only works on alternate Tuesdays).

No, don't thank me. It's all part of the job. I just hope this book helps people (and helps pay off at least some of my bar bills).

Martin Baxendale

OUCH!

The author.

LIFT!

TWINGE!

Repetitive strain injury.

WHY WE GET HANGOVERS

Author's note: Oh come on! We all know <u>why</u> we get hangovers! Can't I skip this bit? The pubs are open!

Editor's note: Just get on with it!!

Author: Duh! Okay! Well in <u>my</u> case it usually goes something like this....

6

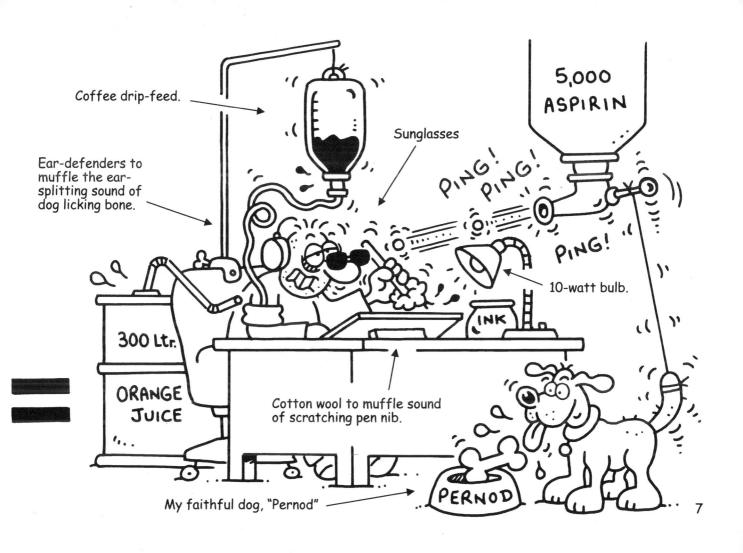

<u>WHY WE GET HANGOVERS</u> - PART 2

Okay, okay! My editor says I've got to put this stuff in too. So here it is (boring, boring, boring)...

Apparently alcohol, like coffee, is a "diuretic", which means it makes you pee a lot (apparently you wee out more than you drink - no, I can't figure that one out either but it's true). Which is why you get dehydrated no matter how much beer you've downed (now they tell me!)

Plus, when there's too much booze in your system for your liver to deal with at its normal rate, it seems the alcohol breaks down into nasty headache-inducing toxins, made worse by chemical impurities already in your drink (red wine and dark spirits are the worst).

On top of that, too much alcohol stimulates your brain when you're asleep so that you're restless, don't get proper deep sleep, and wake up knackered. It also irritates your stomach, which is what makes you feel sick, and can give you diarrhoea.

(And the barman at my local gobbing in my pint just because I haven't paid my bar bill can't help either).

Mrs Baxendale says I'd get fewer hangovers if I didn't come up with "stupid" ideas like this beer dispensing aid that I had made for my last birthday. And here's what <u>she</u> gave me (which would <u>you</u> rather have?)

BASIC HANGOVER CATEGORIES

Of course not all hangovers are the same. They come in varying degrees of severity.

After prolonged study of the different types, I've categorised them into 3 basic levels — a kind of Richter Scale for hangovers.

I've also identified and codified a large number of sub-categories amongst my own hangovers, all subtly different from each other in their degrees and differing proportions of dehydration, pain, nausea, loss of the will to live, and disgust and/or pity elicited from those around me.

But that's just a hobby of mine. Most people will be happy to be able to recognise the following basic levels and their varying demands for action on the part of the sufferer.

CATEGORY 1 HANGOVER

Slight headache.

THROB!

RUMBLE!

OOH! DON'T THINK I CAN GO INTO WORK TODAY!

Mouth a bit dry.

A little bit queasy.

Basic recommended action:
Drink some water or juice, have a fried egg sandwich and sod off to work you wimp! Dear God, I've felt worse than that after a week **off** the booze!!

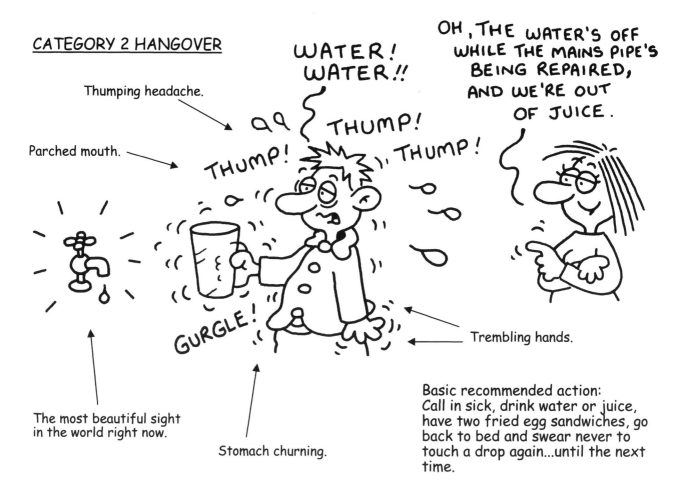

CATEGORY 3 HANGOVER

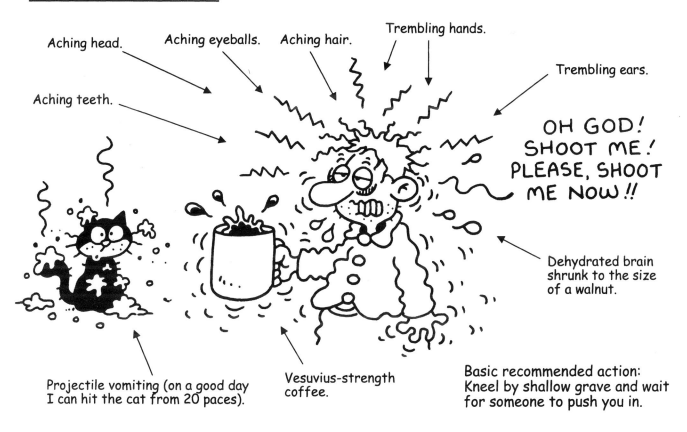

Aching head.

Aching eyeballs.

Aching hair.

Trembling hands.

Trembling ears.

Aching teeth.

OH GOD! SHOOT ME! PLEASE, SHOOT ME NOW!!

Dehydrated brain shrunk to the size of a walnut.

Projectile vomiting (on a good day I can hit the cat from 20 paces).

Vesuvius-strength coffee.

Basic recommended action: Kneel by shallow grave and wait for someone to push you in.

HANGOVER PREVENTION

Prevention is better than cure, they say - usually when they can't cure something. <u>Mrs</u> Baxendale says the chances of curing or stopping <u>me</u> are virtually nil (though that doesn't stop her trying to hide my bottle openers).

But, as she frequently points out (to me, our friends, complete strangers, and on several occasions the police) I'm a particularly hopeless and pathetic case, and thank God not everyone's like me. So here we go...

1) <u>DRINK LOTS OF WATER</u>

Obviously drinking plenty of water can help to stop you dehydrating and prevent or reduce the severity of a hangover.

They say that ideally you should drink some water before you go boozing <u>plus</u> knock back <u>more</u> water in between alcoholic drinks. Yeah, right! <u>That's</u> gonna happen! Oh, sorry, we're not just talking about me....so, yeah! Brilliant idea! Go for it! Why not?

Just don't stray too far from the toilet door!

YES, THIS DRINKING WATER BETWEEN PINTS WORKS! HAVEN'T HAD A HANGOVER ALL WEEK... BUT I HAVE BEEN WEEING MY PANTS IN PUBLIC A BIT MORE THAN USUAL....

I'LL GET YOUR PORTA-LOO....

PSSSSS!

Me making party small-talk.

You're also supposed to drink plenty of water before you go to bed, which I have to admit I do. Mainly because it's easier for <u>Mrs</u> Baxendale to hold me down and get the funnel in my mouth when I'm knackered at the end of the night than in the middle of a party.

Only problem is (especially if you're already full of beer) you're likely to be up and down to the loo all night. Either that, or you spend all night dreaming about peeing and wake up with a bladder the size of a gym ball.

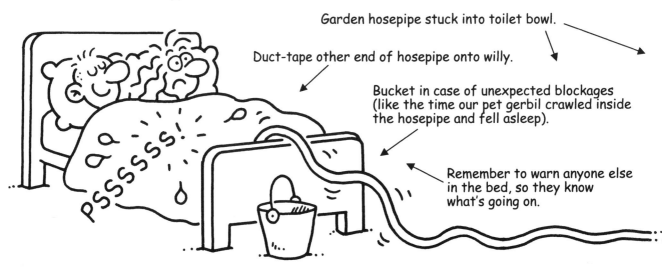

Garden hosepipe stuck into toilet bowl.

Duct-tape other end of hosepipe onto willy.

Bucket in case of unexpected blockages (like the time our pet gerbil crawled inside the hosepipe and fell asleep).

Remember to warn anyone else in the bed, so they know what's going on.

I find the above precaution saves a lot of nightime disturbance and/or embarrassing duvet sogginess. It can also prevent the further embarrassment of being caught drunkenly relieving your bloated bladder in the wardrobe or the potted plant on the landing, in the mistaken belief that you've made it to the loo in time (something that happens so often in our house that <u>Mrs</u> Baxendale has taken to locking her wardrobe door at night......but, for some reason, not mine).

2) <u>DON'T DRINK ON AN EMPTY STOMACH</u>

Not unless you <u>want</u> to end up disgustingly legless, make a complete arse of yourself and wake up with the Mother Of All Hangovers. (Editor's note: Sounds like one of the author's quiet nights in! Hee Hee! Ow!! Who threw that bottle?!!)

And of course drinking <u>with</u> food helps to soak up the alcohol as well as starting with a full stomach, so plenty of snacking during a boozy night out or party helps too.

HOW MANY TIMES HAVE I TOLD YOU NOT TO BRING YOUR OWN FOOD INTO THE BAR ?!

MUNCH! CHOMP!

✓ RIGHT!

X WRONG!

Eight pints and a packet of crisps.

15

3) <u>TRY NOT TO MIX YOUR DRINKS TOO MUCH</u>

Apparently mixing your drinks really can make your hangover worse, because different types of alcoholic drinks contain different kinds of toxic impurities. So if you mix your drinks, that puts extra strain on your liver, which has to cope with a wider range of nasty booze chemicals than if you stuck to one type of hooch.

....RED WINE, SHERRY, BRANDY, VODKA, CIDER, PERNOD.... IS THERE ANYTHING YOU <u>HAVEN'T</u> PUT IN THIS PUNCH?!

SLICE OF ORANGE?

RECIPE

Also, try to avoid too much red wine and dark-coloured spirits in one session, as these can be particularly hangover-inducing. White wine and clear spirits, like vodka, tend to be a safer bet (which is brill 'cos it means you can drink more of them!! ... Will someone please tell <u>Mrs</u> Baxendale to stop looking at me like that!)

MR BAX V. HIS LIVER - A CAUTIONARY TALE OF A DEFEATED ORGAN

4) BETTER QUALITY BOOZE = LESS HANGOVER RISK

It's also true that, generally speaking, more expensive and better quality booze is likely to be less hangover-inducing than lower quality and dirt-cheap alcoholic drinks.

Home-brew wine and beer can be very high in hangover-producing chemical by-products if made with cheap ingredients like white sugar. Cheaper spirits may be less highly refined, and therefore less pure, than more expensive versions. And the cheapest wines can be higher in chemical additives and stomach-upsetting acidity than higher priced ones.

Organic wines are said to be less likely to give you a hangover because they tend to contain less sulphur as a preservative than non-organic.

And as for my home-distilled rhubarb and turnip gin, after it was confiscated by Customs and Excise it was found to be a very effective chemical weapon of mass destruction, now banned by international treaty (although small stocks are held in high-security labs for research purposes).

BEFORE YOU TRY THE HOME-MADE BRUSSEL SPROUT AND BANANA-SKIN WINE, COULD I JUST ASK YOU TO SIGN THESE ACCIDENTAL-DEATH LAWSUIT WAIVER FORMS....

Of course, you could do what I always do when I'm throwing a party: Give the guests the cheapo booze to drink, while hiding any bottles of good stuff that they bring, for my own private consumption.

Conversely, when invited to other people's parties be sure to take a grotty bottle of cheap rot-gut and then go straight for the host's private stock of the good stuff (but not if you're coming to one of my parties, you cheapskate bastards!)

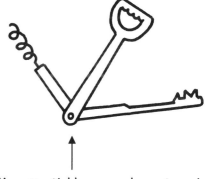

My essential home made party-going tool - combined bottle-opener, corkscrew and lock-pick.

19

5) DRINK SLOWER (YEAH, RIGHT!)

Health experts recommend that to help avoid hangovers you shouldn't drink too quickly. It seems the liver can only process alcohol properly at the rate of up to roughly one drink per hour. Drinking faster than that increases the chances of having a hangover in the morning.

Mrs Baxendale's always on at me to slow down and make my drinks last longer, and I always thought "Yeah! That's gonna happen!" but it's amazing what you can do with a bit of will-power.

OKAY, I'LL TRY TO MAKE THIS ONE LAST AN HOUR...

The experts also say that women tend to process alcohol slower than men (because of differences in body chemical levels) so should be even more careful not to drink too fast - and should not try to keep up with the male drinkers in a group.

GLUG! GLUG! GLUG! GLUG! GLUG! GLUG!

AS IF I COULD EVEN HOPE TO KEEP UP WITH THAT!

Plus of course women tend to have lower body weights, so can usually tolerate less total alcohol consumption before risking getting a hangover. Sorry!

COPING WITH HANGOVERS

1) BE PREPARED!

Sometimes, despite all your best intentions (ahem!), at the end of the night you just <u>know</u> you're going to be horrendously hungover in the morning. And that's the time to start planning, even if all you want to do is fall into bed. Because I've always found that a little advance preparation can save a lot of time and trouble when you wake up...

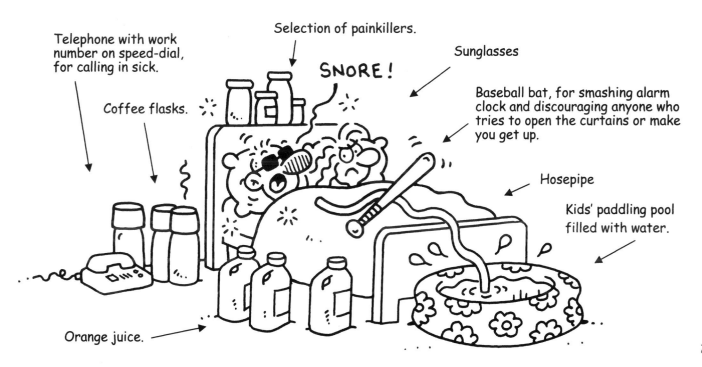

Telephone with work number on speed-dial, for calling in sick.

Coffee flasks.

Selection of painkillers.

SNORE!

Sunglasses

Baseball bat, for smashing alarm clock and discouraging anyone who tries to open the curtains or make you get up.

Hosepipe

Kids' paddling pool filled with water.

Orange juice.

2) <u>RE-HYDRATE</u> (DRINK LOTS OF WATER!)

The first and most important thing is to reverse your après-binge dehydration. In my case, dehydration is usually so advanced that <u>Mrs</u> Baxendale has to implement our own specially developed intensive emergency re-hydration procedures (before I crumble into a tiny pile of desiccated dust like a sunbathing Count Dracula).

Dried-out body soaking up water through feet, like a shrivelled sponge.

Getting plenty of water back into your system will help relieve some of the worst hangover symptoms. Taking vitamin-C (especially high-dose soluble) and multi-vitamins at the same time will help your body to deal with those hangover toxins and further speed recovery.

3) <u>FOOD AND DRINK REMEDIES</u>

When you've got a hangover, eating and drinking the right things helps to relieve your symptoms and shorten the agony.

Water, of course, to re-hydrate you, but also fruit juice (and fresh fruit). The fructose in it gives you a quick energy boost and helps your body clean out the toxins quicker, as will the vitamin-C.

A high-dose vitamin-C tab and a multivitamin will also help, and a sport-drink will provide a further energy boost and help correct body salt imbalances.

Bananas are good. You lose a lot of vital potassium from your system when you drink too much alcohol (it's washed out in all that weeing that booze makes you do) which makes you feel grotty. Bananas, being very rich in potassium, help correct that.

Eggs too contain a chemical that's very good at helping deal with hangover toxins, so are an ideal hangover breakfast choice. Many people think burnt toast is good, but apparently that's just a myth.

X WRONG!

Bottle of beer.

DIP! DIP!

Last night's leftover pizza and curry sauce.

✓ RIGHT!

Orange juice.

Banana smoothie.

Ooh, look! It's <u>Mrs</u> Baxendale with a <u>hangover</u>! I thought she <u>never</u> drank too much!!

GROAN!

My favourite hangover breakfast — fried egg and aspirin sandwich.

MUNCH!

CRUNCH!

Soft-boiled egg.

Vitamin-C and Multi-vits.

Aspirin is a good painkiller for hangover-induced headaches (but not if you know you're allergic!) It's also been found to help reduce hangover symptoms if a small dose is taken at bedtime (but not, not, NOT if you're allergic, okay?!!) And it can cause stomach-ache if you have a sensitive tum, so go easy with the dose.

24

The "Hair Of The Dog" is not recommended by health experts (the bastards!!) It seems (unless they're lying!) that you'll only feel worse in the long-run even if a quick drink peps you up in the short-term.

Coffee too will perk you up at first, and help relieve that pounding head, but (oh dear God!) too much will add to the jitters and anxiety that hang-overs can produce, make you more tired later when the caffeine wears off, and dehy-drate you more unless taken with plenty of water (but it smells so goooooood!!!)

I FEEL MUCH BETTER AFTER THAT SECOND LITRE OF COFFEE! D'YOU LIKE THE CARTOON I'VE DRAWN FOR MY NEXT BOOK?

4) TO EXERCISE OR REST?

Mrs Baxendale says get your lazy arse out of bed and go to the gym. I say stay in bed and fester.

The health experts say I'm right. Yes!! Ouch! Will someone please tell Mrs Baxendale that's not what corkscrews are for (and help me get it out! She's ruined my underpants!).

Okay, it depends. If you're really badly hungover, rest and sleep are the best cure. So staying in bed is a good idea (see! I told you!)

Very <u>hard</u> exercise (like running or a workout at the gym) <u>isn't</u> recommended, despite what <u>some</u> people might say. In fact it can make things worse by adding to your dehydration and fatigue, and won't help get rid of the toxins any faster (despite the myths about "sweating" the booze toxins out). Also cold showers don't really make any physical difference.

But once you feel up to it, lighter exercise like a walk, or a bit of not-too-strenuous <u>nookies</u> (note from <u>Mrs</u> Baxendale: You wish!!) will help get your blood circulation going, put some natural feel-good endorphins into your system and generally make you feel a lot better.

5) COPING WITH A HANGOVER AT WORK

When you absolutely <u>have</u> to go into work despite a bad hangover (e.g. you've called in "sick" loads of times this month already, and your boss is getting suspicious) then obviously your main problem is how to sleep it off in the workplace without getting fired.

If you have a desk to work at, the answer is simple with the help of the patented Baxendale "Wide Awake" office disguise:

I've personally spent many hours happily snoozing at my desk with the help of this disguise, when <u>Mrs</u> Baxendale has forced me back to work despite a thumping hangover (she really knows how to use an electric cattle prod!)

Discreet wrist-bands with springs on suckers attached to desk top, make your hands bounce around over key-board, calculator, paperwork, etc as if you're wide awake and working.

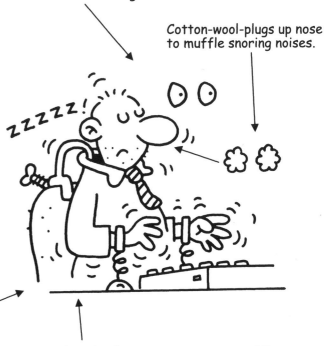

Cut ping-pong ball in half and paint to look like wide-awake eyeballs. Stick over closed eyes before nodding off.

Cotton-wool-plugs up nose to muffle snoring noises.

Chair-back support stops you nodding and falling forward across your desk.

If you don't have a desk then you'll need to find somewhere else to sleep off your hangover, and the toilet is usually your best bet.

Remember to sneak a pillow into work with you (toilet cisterns are cold and hard). And I always find the following little device will help put your boss (or in my case, <u>Mrs Baxendale</u>) off the idea of investigating too closely into why the toilet is occupied for such long periods.

The patented Baxendale "Diarrhoea Simulator".

SPLLURRP!

Record sound of hot-water-bottle full of custard being squirted into bucket over and over again. Add appropriate groans and agonised moans. Play back while you snooze in the loo wearing earplugs.

SPLLURRRP!

STAFF TOILET

SPLLURRP!

SPLLURRP!

SPLLURRP!

I would also strongly recommend you use this third hangover work-aid if your job depends a lot on very accurate data-inputting or having very steady hands, and where one little shaking-hand, hangover-induced slip of the finger can have dire consequences.

For example, if you're an air-traffic controller, nuclear submarine missile targeting and launch operator, brain surgeon, or supermarket check-out person (my local supermarket overcharged me three quid on a bottle of scotch last week!)

Paper-shredder button.

Nuclear missiles launch button.

PRIME MINISTER

Tight-fitting adjustable wrist-hoop fixed to desk-top with metal rod and rubber sucker, helps hold shaky hand steady.

Originally devised to help hold my shaky hand steady for drawing after heavy nights out on the town, this is equally useful for keyboard work where accuracy is vital (i.e. obviously not places like tax credits offices or railway timetable offices) or other very important workplaces.

OTHER BOOKS BY MARTIN BAXENDALE:

'THE SNOWDROP GARDEN' - Martin's first novel is a wickedly
funny and heart-warming tale of love, misunderstandings and a last-ditch
attempt to save one of England's most beautiful woodland snowdrop
gardens from the builders' bulldozers. A really great, laugh-out-loud
read.

'WHEN WILL MY BABY BRAIN FALL OUT?' - Martin's first children's book. Seven-year-old Millie struggles
with her maths homework but then she gets hold of the idea that things will be better when her 'baby brain' falls out, just
like a baby tooth, and her cleverer big-girl brain grows in its place. Should Mum and Dad put her straight or play along?
A very funny yet charming story that will have children laughing out loud.

And some of Martin's best-selling cartoon gift-books:

'Your New Baby, An Owner's Manual' (over 500,000 copies sold).
'How To Be A Baby, An Instruction Manual For Newborns'
'Your Marriage, An Owner's Manual'
'How To Be Married, An Instruction Manual For Newlyweds'
'Life After 40, A Survival Guide For Women'
'Life After 40, A Survival Guide For Men'
'Life After 50, A Survival Guide For Women'
'Life After 50, A Survival Guide For Men'
'How To Stay Awake During Sex (and other handy hints on coping with old age)'
'Martin Baxendale's Better Sex Guide'
'The Relationship Survival Guide'
'A Very Rude Book About Willies'
'The Cat Owner's Survival Guide'
'The Dog Owner's Survival Guide'
'Your Man, An Owner's Manual'
'Calm Down!! The Stress Survival Guide'
'Your Pregnancy, A Survival Guide'
'Women Are Wonderful, Men Are A Mess'

These and other books by Martin Baxendale can be
ordered from www.amazon.co.uk (search for Martin
Baxendale, or search by title, in 'books') and from
other online bookstores or any High Street bookshop.